Key Stage 2

Fractions

Steve Mills and Hilary Koll

Name _____

Schofield & Sims

Introduction

You might ask why you need to know about fractions. Well, fractions are important because we use them every day when we want to describe parts of whole things – quarter of an hour, half of a cake, a third of the class... etc. In this learning workbook you will find information about how to recognise and write fractions. You will practise working with fractions, and so build a better understanding of them.

How to use this book

Before you start using this book, write your name in the name box on the first page.

Then decide how to begin. If you want a complete course on fractions, you should work right through the book from beginning to end. Another way to use the book is to dip into it when you want to find out about a particular topic. The contents page will help you to find the pages you need.

Whichever way you choose, don't try to do too much at once – it's better to work through the book in short bursts.

When you have found the topic you want to study, look out for these icons, which mark different parts of the text:

Activities

This icon shows you the activities that you should complete. You write your answers in the spaces provided. You might find it useful to have some scrap paper to work on for some of the activities. After you have worked through all the activities on the page, turn to pages A1 to A3 at the centre of the book to check your answers. When you are sure that you understand the topic, put a tick in the box beside it on the Contents page.

On pages 11 and 17, you will find **Progress Tests**. These contain questions that will check your understanding of the topics that you have worked through so far. Check your answers on page A4. It is important that you correct any mistakes before moving on to the next section.

At the back of the book you will find a **Final Test**. This will check your understanding of all the topics (page 26).

Explanation

This text explains the topic and gives examples. Make sure you read it before you start the activities.

Scrap Paper

This icon tells you when you may need to use scrap paper to work out your answers.

Fascinating Facts

This text gives you useful background information about the subject.

Contents

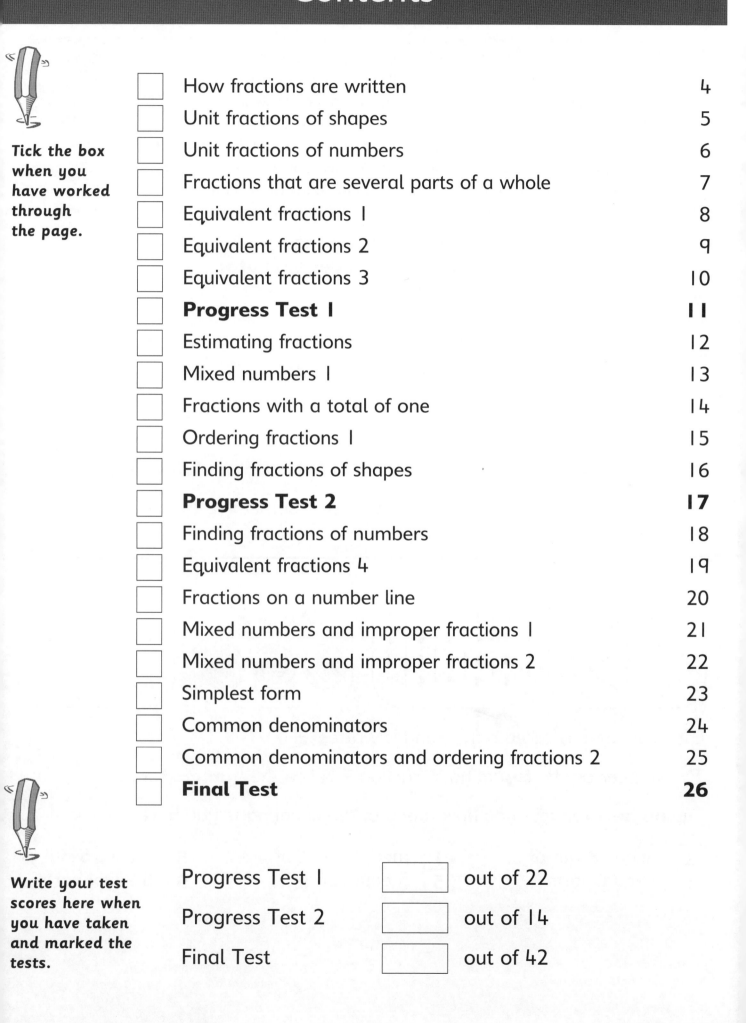

Tick the box when you have worked through the page.

☐	How fractions are written	4
☐	Unit fractions of shapes	5
☐	Unit fractions of numbers	6
☐	Fractions that are several parts of a whole	7
☐	Equivalent fractions 1	8
☐	Equivalent fractions 2	9
☐	Equivalent fractions 3	10
☐	**Progress Test 1**	**11**
☐	Estimating fractions	12
☐	Mixed numbers 1	13
☐	Fractions with a total of one	14
☐	Ordering fractions 1	15
☐	Finding fractions of shapes	16
☐	**Progress Test 2**	**17**
☐	Finding fractions of numbers	18
☐	Equivalent fractions 4	19
☐	Fractions on a number line	20
☐	Mixed numbers and improper fractions 1	21
☐	Mixed numbers and improper fractions 2	22
☐	Simplest form	23
☐	Common denominators	24
☐	Common denominators and ordering fractions 2	25
☐	**Final Test**	**26**

Write your test scores here when you have taken and marked the tests.

Progress Test 1   ☐   out of 22

Progress Test 2   ☐   out of 14

Final Test   ☐   out of 42

How fractions are written

Fractions help us to describe **parts** of whole things.
They are written using a **numerator** and a **denominator**.

How fractions are written

Fractions have one number on top of another.

The number on the **bottom** is called the **denominator** ⟶ $\frac{3}{5}$

These fractions are related: they all have a denominator of 5 ⟶ $\frac{4}{5}$ $\frac{1}{5}$ $\frac{5}{5}$ $\frac{9}{5}$

Fractions with a denominator of **5** are parts of something that have been split into **5 equal parts**, like these:

a whole shape	a whole set of items	a whole pound	a whole line
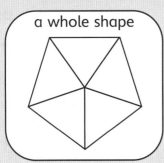			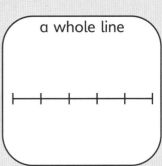

Each part here is called a **fifth** and is written $\frac{1}{5}$

The number on the **top** of your fraction is called the **numerator** ⟶ $\frac{3}{5}$

The **numerator** tells you how many of the equal parts you have.

$\frac{3}{5}$ means **3** out of 5 equal parts

$\frac{1}{5}$ means **1** out of 5 equal parts

$\frac{5}{5}$ means **5** out of 5 equal parts

Unit fractions are fractions with a numerator of **1**, like $\frac{1}{2}$, $\frac{1}{4}$, $\frac{1}{8}$ and $\frac{1}{10}$

Let's start by looking at unit fractions of shapes.

Unit fractions of shapes

The fraction $\frac{1}{5}$ (one fifth) tells us what part of this whole shape is shaded.

$\frac{1}{5}$ → → **1** part of the shape is shaded
out of **5** equal parts *altogether*

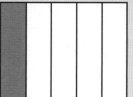

For unit fractions, the numerator will always be **1**.
To find the denominator of a fraction, *count the number of parts altogether.*

1. What fraction of each shape is shaded?   **a)**

b) 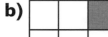   **c)** 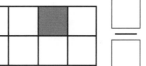   **d)**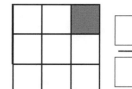

e)    **f)**    **g)**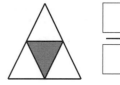

2. Colour these fractions.

a) 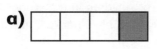 $\frac{1}{3}$ **b)** $\frac{1}{8}$ **c)** $\frac{1}{5}$

3. Tick the fractions shaded that are **correctly** named, and **cross** those that are **incorrect**.

a)  $\frac{1}{3}$ **b)** $\frac{1}{5}$ **c)**  $\frac{1}{6}$

d) 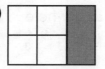 $\frac{1}{5}$ **e)**  $\frac{1}{2}$ **f)** 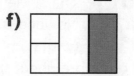 $\frac{1}{3}$

Unit fractions of numbers

We can also find unit fractions **of numbers**. Remember that unit fractions always have a numerator of 1, like $\frac{1}{2}$, $\frac{1}{4}$, $\frac{1}{8}$ and $\frac{1}{10}$

Unit fractions of numbers

To find a fraction of a number, split the number into equal parts or groups by dividing by the bottom number (the denominator).

$\frac{1}{5}$ of 10   Split 10 into 5 equal parts

 2 2   2   2   2

$10 \div 5 = 2$

It's just like division, so finding $\frac{1}{5}$ of 10 is the same as dividing 10 by 5.

1. Share the buttons into equal groups to answer the questions.

a) $\frac{1}{2}$ of 8

b) $\frac{1}{3}$ of 9

2. Divide the number by the denominator to answer these.

a) $\frac{1}{6}$ of 18 = _____

b) $\frac{1}{10}$ of 50 = _____

c) $\frac{1}{3}$ of 15 = _____

d) $\frac{1}{5}$ of 20 = _____

3. Answer these questions mentally.

a) A man earned £60. He gave **one tenth** to charity. How much did he give?

b) **One quarter** of a class of 24 children is boys. How many are boys?

c) There are 100 pages in a book. **One fifth** of the pages contain pictures. How many pages contain pictures?

d) **One eighth** of the children in a school have packed lunch. There are 160 children in the school. How many have packed lunch?

Did you know... The Ancient Egyptians only used unit fractions. Nowadays we use fractions that are several parts of a whole (with numerators that are numbers more than 1), like $\frac{2}{3}$, $\frac{3}{4}$, $\frac{6}{8}$. Find out more about them on the next page.

Fractions that are several parts of a whole

We can find other fractions as well as unit fractions.

To find other fractions **of shapes**:

- count the number of equal parts in each shape.
  This is the **denominator** of the fraction.

- count how many of these equal parts
  are shaded.
  This is the **numerator** of the fraction.

 $\frac{7}{8}$ of this shape is shaded.

1. What fraction of each shape is shaded?   **a)**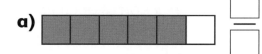

b)    **c)**    **d)**

e)   **f)**    **g)**

This is the same for sets of objects:

- count the number of counters below. This is the **denominator**.

- count the number of counters that are shaded. This is the **numerator**.

What fraction of these counters is shaded?

Seven out of ten objects are shaded,
so $\frac{7}{10}$ of the counters is shaded.

2. What fraction of these objects is shaded?

a)    **b)**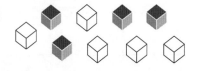

c)   **d)**

Equivalent fractions 1

Equivalent fractions are fractions that stand for the same amount.

They can look very different but are actually worth the same!

Here are some equivalent fractions.

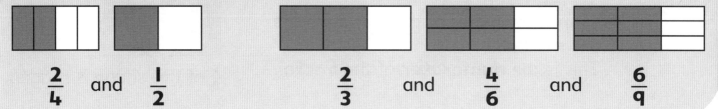

$\frac{2}{4}$ and $\frac{1}{2}$ $\frac{2}{3}$ and $\frac{4}{6}$ and $\frac{6}{9}$

1. A fraction of each flag is shaded. Join any flags with the same fraction of shaded.

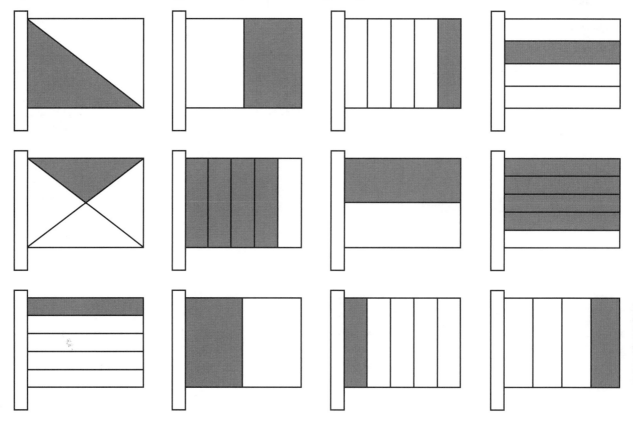

2. Write the fraction of each rectangle that is shaded. Join any equivalent fractions.

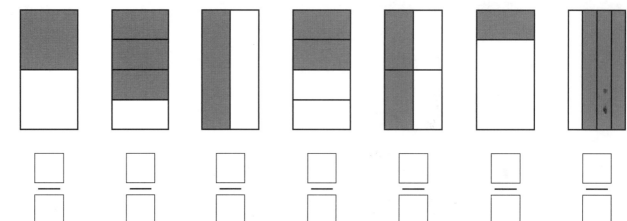

To check whether two or more fractions are equivalent you can shade the fractions of a shape and compare them, like this:

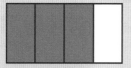 $\frac{3}{4}$

 $\frac{4}{5}$

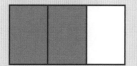 $\frac{2}{3}$

$\frac{8}{10}$

So we can see that $\frac{3}{4}$ is larger than $\frac{2}{3}$ $\frac{4}{5}$ is equivalent to $\frac{8}{10}$

1. Shade the two fractions in each pair and write which is larger or whether they are equivalent.

a) $\frac{3}{4}$

$\frac{7}{8}$

_____

b) $\frac{1}{5}$

$\frac{1}{4}$

_____

c) $\frac{2}{5}$

$\frac{4}{10}$

_____

d) $\frac{3}{4}$

$\frac{5}{6}$

_____

e) $\frac{2}{3}$

$\frac{6}{8}$

_____

f) $\frac{3}{5}$

$\frac{9}{15}$

_____

2. Write the fractions for each diagram to show pairs of equivalent fractions.

a)

b)

c)

d)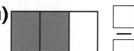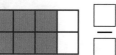

e)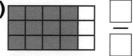

f)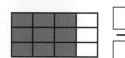

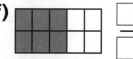

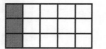

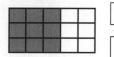

Equivalent fractions 3

 1. Join any equivalent fractions you can see.
Sketch and shade shapes if you need to.

 $\frac{1}{2}$ $\frac{1}{4}$ $\frac{3}{4}$ $\frac{2}{4}$ $\frac{6}{8}$

 $\frac{2}{6}$ $\frac{1}{3}$ $\frac{3}{12}$ $\frac{5}{10}$

 2. Write the fraction of sweets in each bag that is purple.
Join any equivalent fractions.

a)

b)

c)

_____   _____   _____

d)

e)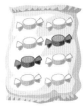

f)

_____   _____   _____

g)

h)

i)

_____   _____   _____

3. Write a fraction that is equivalent to:

a) $\frac{1}{2}$ _____

b) $\frac{1}{3}$ _____

c) $\frac{2}{3}$ _____

d) $\frac{1}{4}$ _____

e) $\frac{3}{4}$ _____

f) $\frac{1}{5}$ _____

1. What fraction of each shape is shaded? **a)**

b) 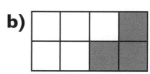 **c)**  **d)**

2. Divide the number by the denominator to answer these.

a) $\frac{1}{6}$ of 24 = _____

b) $\frac{1}{10}$ of 30 = _____

c) $\frac{1}{3}$ of 12 = _____

d) $\frac{1}{5}$ of 25 = _____

3. Answer these questions mentally.

a) A man earned £40. He gave **one tenth** to charity. How much did he give?

b) **One quarter** of a class of 36 children is girls. How many are girls?

c) There are 50 pages in a book. **One fifth** of the pages contain pictures. How many pages contain pictures?

d) **One eighth** of the children in a school have packed lunch. There are 240 children in the school. How many have packed lunch?

4. Work these out mentally.

a) $\frac{3}{8}$ of 32 _____

b) $\frac{5}{6}$ of 24 _____

c) $\frac{2}{9}$ of 45 _____

5. Write the fraction of each tile that is shaded. Join any equivalent fractions.

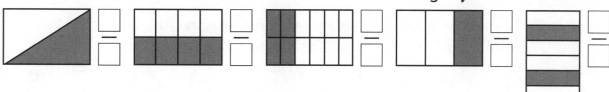

6. Write **two** fractions that are equivalent to:

a) $\frac{1}{3}$ _____

b) $\frac{2}{5}$ _____

Estimating fractions

Fractions are all around us. We use them every day.

> It's **quarter** past three.

> Do you want **half** an apple?

> A **third** of this pie has gone.

> It's nearly **half** time.

Because we use fractions so much it is useful to be able to **estimate** them.

 1. About how much of these cakes have **not** been eaten?

a) 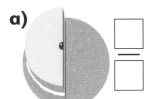   b) 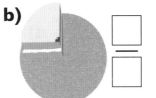   c) 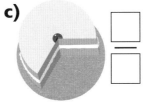   d)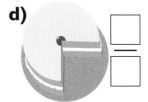

 2. About how much of these circles is **missing**?

a)   b)   c)    d)

 3. About what time is it?

a) 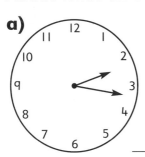   b) 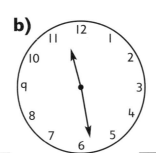   c)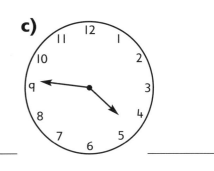

_____   _____   _____

 4. These jars hold 100 sweets when they are full.
About how many sweets are in each of these jars?

a)    b)    c)    d)

_____   _____   _____

Mixed numbers 1

Did you know...? Numbers like $3\frac{1}{2}$, $4\frac{1}{4}$ and $6\frac{3}{4}$ are called **mixed numbers** because they are a mix of whole numbers, like **3**, **4** and **6**, and fractions, like $\frac{1}{2}$, $\frac{1}{4}$ and $\frac{3}{4}$.

$3\frac{1}{4}$ glasses of juice

1. Match the mixed numbers to the correct pictures.

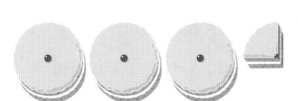

$1\frac{3}{4}$

$2\frac{1}{4}$

$2\frac{1}{2}$

$3\frac{1}{4}$

$3\frac{1}{2}$

$4\frac{1}{3}$

$4\frac{7}{10}$

$5\frac{3}{10}$

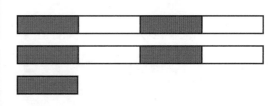

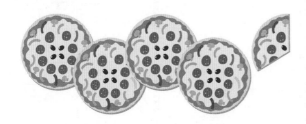

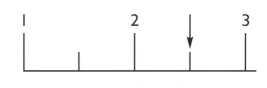

2. Continue these patterns.

a) $\frac{1}{4}$ $\frac{1}{2}$ $\frac{3}{4}$ 1 $1\frac{1}{4}$ ___ ___ ___ ___ ___

b) $3\frac{1}{3}$ $3\frac{2}{3}$ 4 $4\frac{1}{3}$ ___ ___ ___ ___

Understanding Maths | Schofield & Sims

Fractions   **13**

Fractions with a total of one

Do you remember that fractions are equal parts of things?

So $\frac{3}{4}$ means something split into four equal parts and we have three of them. If we get one more part we will have the whole thing.

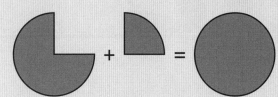

So three quarters and one quarter makes four quarters and four quarters is the same as one whole.

$\frac{3}{4} + \frac{1}{4} = \frac{4}{4}$ and $\frac{4}{4}$ is the same as **1** whole.

In the same way $\frac{1}{3} + \frac{2}{3} = $ **1** and $\frac{2}{7} + \frac{5}{7} = $ **1**

1. Find pairs of fractions with a total of **1** from the grid and write them below.

$\frac{2}{3}$	$\frac{1}{6}$	$\frac{5}{8}$	$\frac{1}{2}$
$\frac{1}{7}$	$\frac{1}{4}$	$\frac{3}{7}$	$\frac{3}{10}$
$\frac{9}{10}$	$\frac{7}{8}$	$\frac{3}{8}$	$\frac{3}{4}$
$\frac{6}{7}$	$\frac{1}{9}$	$\frac{4}{9}$	$\frac{2}{5}$
$\frac{7}{10}$	$\frac{1}{5}$	$\frac{1}{3}$	$\frac{1}{2}$
$\frac{5}{9}$	$\frac{3}{5}$	$\frac{5}{6}$	$\frac{4}{5}$
$\frac{1}{8}$	$\frac{4}{7}$	$\frac{1}{10}$	$\frac{8}{9}$

$\frac{2}{3} + \frac{1}{3} = $ **1** $\dfrac{\square}{\square} + \dfrac{\square}{\square} = $ **1**

$\dfrac{\square}{\square} + \dfrac{\square}{\square} = $ **1** $\dfrac{\square}{\square} + \dfrac{\square}{\square} = $ **1**

$\dfrac{\square}{\square} + \dfrac{\square}{\square} = $ **1** $\dfrac{\square}{\square} + \dfrac{\square}{\square} = $ **1**

$\dfrac{\square}{\square} + \dfrac{\square}{\square} = $ **1** $\dfrac{\square}{\square} + \dfrac{\square}{\square} = $ **1**

$\dfrac{\square}{\square} + \dfrac{\square}{\square} = $ **1** $\dfrac{\square}{\square} + \dfrac{\square}{\square} = $ **1**

$\dfrac{\square}{\square} + \dfrac{\square}{\square} = $ **1** $\dfrac{\square}{\square} + \dfrac{\square}{\square} = $ **1**

$\dfrac{\square}{\square} + \dfrac{\square}{\square} = $ **1** $\dfrac{\square}{\square} + \dfrac{\square}{\square} = $ **1**

Answers to Activities

Page 5

1. a) $\frac{1}{6}$
   b) $\frac{1}{6}$ c) $\frac{1}{8}$ d) $\frac{1}{9}$
   e) $\frac{1}{4}$ f) $\frac{1}{3}$ g) $\frac{1}{4}$

2. Any one section shaded in each shape

3. a) ✗ b) ✓ c) ✗
   d) ✗ e) ✗ f) ✓

Page 6

1. a) 4 b) 3
2. a) 3 b) 5 c) 5 d) 4
3. a) £6 b) 6 c) 20 d) 20

Page 7

1. a) $\frac{5}{6}$
   b) $\frac{1}{2}$ or $\frac{3}{6}$ c) $\frac{5}{8}$ d) $\frac{4}{9}$
   e) $\frac{3}{4}$ f) $\frac{2}{3}$ g) $\frac{3}{4}$

2. a) $\frac{5}{8}$ b) $\frac{4}{9}$ c) $\frac{5}{12}$ d) $\frac{11}{15}$

Page 8

1.
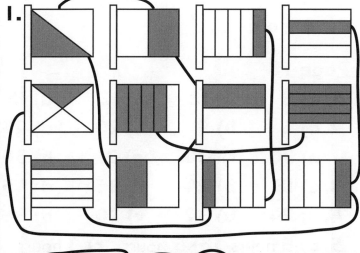

2.
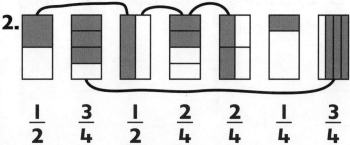

$\frac{1}{2}$ $\frac{3}{4}$ $\frac{1}{2}$ $\frac{2}{4}$ $\frac{2}{4}$ $\frac{1}{4}$ $\frac{3}{4}$

Page 9

1. a) **3** parts and **7** parts shaded, $\frac{7}{8}$ is larger
   b) **1** part and **1** part shaded, $\frac{1}{4}$ is larger
   c) **2** parts and **4** parts shaded, they are equivalent
   d) **3** parts and **5** parts shaded, $\frac{5}{6}$ is larger
   e) **2** parts and **6** parts shaded, $\frac{6}{8}$ is larger
   f) **3** parts and **9** parts shaded, they are equivalent

2. a) $\frac{2}{3}$, $\frac{4}{6}$ b) $\frac{12}{15}$, $\frac{4}{5}$ c) $\frac{3}{4}$, $\frac{9}{12}$
   d) $\frac{6}{8}$, $\frac{12}{16}$ e) $\frac{1}{5}$, $\frac{3}{15}$ f) $\frac{6}{10}$, $\frac{9}{15}$

Page 10

1. $\frac{1}{2}$ joined to $\frac{2}{4}$ and $\frac{5}{10}$
    $\frac{1}{3}$ joined to $\frac{2}{6}$
    $\frac{1}{4}$ joined to $\frac{3}{12}$
    $\frac{3}{4}$ joined to $\frac{6}{8}$

2. a) $\frac{1}{2}$ b) $\frac{1}{3}$ c) $\frac{1}{4}$
   d) $\frac{2}{6}$ or $\frac{1}{3}$ e) $\frac{2}{8}$ or $\frac{1}{4}$ f) $\frac{2}{4}$ or $\frac{1}{2}$
   g) $\frac{3}{4}$ h) $\frac{3}{6}$ or $\frac{1}{2}$ i) $\frac{6}{8}$ or $\frac{3}{4}$
   a), f) and h) joined
   b) and d) joined
   c) and e) joined
   g) and i) joined

3. Any equivalent fraction, e.g.
   a) $\frac{2}{4}$ or $\frac{5}{10}$ b) $\frac{2}{6}$ or $\frac{10}{30}$ c) $\frac{4}{6}$ or $\frac{8}{12}$
   d) $\frac{2}{8}$ or $\frac{10}{40}$ e) $\frac{6}{8}$ or $\frac{30}{40}$ f) $\frac{3}{15}$ or $\frac{5}{25}$

Answers to Activities

1. a) $\frac{1}{2}$ **b)** $\frac{1}{4}$ **c)** $\frac{2}{3}$ **d)** $\frac{3}{4}$

2. a) $\frac{1}{2}$ **b)** $\frac{1}{4}$ **c)** $\frac{2}{3}$ **d)** $\frac{3}{4}$

3. a) $\frac{1}{4}$ past **2**   **b)** $\frac{1}{2}$ past **11**

  c) $\frac{1}{4}$ to **5**

4. a) about **50**   **b)** about **25**

  c) about **75**   **d)** about **33**

  (accept answers +/– 5 in each case)

Page 13

1.

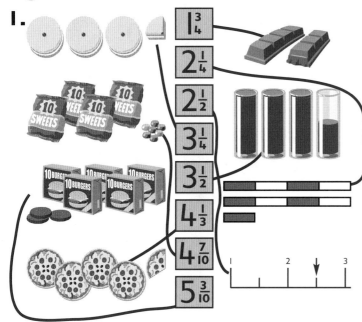

2. a) $1\frac{1}{2}$, $1\frac{3}{4}$, 2, $2\frac{1}{4}$, $2\frac{1}{2}$, $2\frac{3}{4}$

  b) $4\frac{2}{3}$, 5, $5\frac{1}{3}$, $5\frac{2}{3}$, 6

Page 14

1. The following pairs in any order

  $(\frac{2}{3} + \frac{1}{3})$ $\frac{5}{8} + \frac{3}{8}$

  $\frac{1}{2} + \frac{1}{2}$ $\frac{1}{7} + \frac{6}{7}$

  $\frac{1}{4} + \frac{3}{4}$ $\frac{2}{5} + \frac{3}{5}$

  $\frac{3}{10} + \frac{7}{10}$ $\frac{9}{10} + \frac{1}{10}$

  $\frac{7}{8} + \frac{1}{8}$ $\frac{1}{9} + \frac{8}{9}$

  $\frac{4}{9} + \frac{5}{9}$ $\frac{1}{5} + \frac{4}{5}$

  $\frac{3}{7} + \frac{4}{7}$ $\frac{1}{6} + \frac{5}{6}$

Page 15

1. Less than $\frac{1}{2}$

  $\frac{1}{8}$ $\frac{3}{7}$ $\frac{2}{5}$ $\frac{4}{9}$

  $\frac{3}{8}$ $\frac{4}{10}$ $\frac{1}{3}$

Greater than $\frac{1}{2}$

  $\frac{5}{6}$ $\frac{3}{4}$ $\frac{7}{10}$ $\frac{4}{5}$ $\frac{4}{7}$

  $\frac{5}{8}$ $\frac{3}{5}$ $\frac{5}{9}$ $\frac{2}{3}$

2. a) $\frac{7}{8}$, $\frac{3}{4}$, $\frac{1}{2}$, $\frac{1}{4}$, $\frac{1}{8}$

  b) $\frac{5}{6}$, $\frac{2}{3}$, $\frac{1}{2}$, $\frac{1}{3}$, $\frac{1}{6}$

  c) $\frac{9}{10}$, $\frac{4}{5}$, $\frac{1}{2}$, $\frac{1}{5}$, $\frac{1}{10}$

Page 16

1. a) **3** squares shaded

  b) **1** rectangle shaded

  c) **3** rectangles shaded

  d) **2** triangles shaded

  e) **6** sectors shaded

  f) **5** squares shaded

  g) **3** squares shaded

  h) **2** rhombi shaded

2. a) $\frac{2}{5}$ **b)** $\frac{1}{4}$

  c) $\frac{3}{12}$ or $\frac{1}{4}$ **d)** $\frac{2}{7}$

Page 18

1. a) 8   **b)** 12   **c)** 12   **d)** 15

2. a) 6   **b)** 9   **c)** 20   **d)** 25

  e) 30   **f)** 30   **g)** 21   **h)** 56

3. a) 18   **b)** 24   **c)** 36   **d)** 45

4. a) 24   **b)** 32   **c)** 20   **d)** 36

5. a) **6** hours **b)** **5** hours **c)** **9** hours

  d) **4** hours

Answers to Activities

Page 19

1. Sets in any order:

$\frac{1}{2}$ $\frac{5}{10}$ $\frac{6}{12}$ $\frac{10}{20}$ $\frac{50}{100}$

$\frac{3}{8}$ $\frac{6}{16}$

$\frac{5}{6}$ $\frac{10}{12}$ $\frac{15}{18}$

$\frac{1}{4}$ $\frac{2}{8}$ $\frac{4}{16}$

$\frac{4}{10}$ $\frac{2}{5}$ $\frac{8}{20}$ $\frac{16}{40}$

$\frac{1}{5}$ $\frac{4}{20}$ $\frac{5}{25}$ $\frac{2}{10}$ $\frac{3}{15}$

$\frac{1}{7}$ $\frac{2}{14}$

$\frac{2}{6}$ $\frac{1}{3}$ $\frac{5}{15}$ $\frac{3}{9}$ $\frac{4}{12}$ $\frac{10}{30}$

2. Two extra equivalent fractions correctly added to each set

Page 20

1. a)

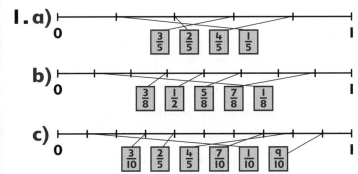

b)

c)

2. a) $\frac{1}{9}$, $\frac{1}{3}$, $\frac{5}{9}$, $\frac{2}{3}$, $\frac{7}{9}$

b) $\frac{1}{12}$, $\frac{1}{6}$, $\frac{2}{6}$, $\frac{5}{12}$, $\frac{7}{12}$, $\frac{2}{3}$, $\frac{5}{6}$

Page 21

1. a) $1\frac{1}{2}$ b) $3\frac{1}{2}$ c) $1\frac{2}{3}$ d) $1\frac{3}{4}$

e) $1\frac{7}{10}$ f) $2\frac{3}{5}$ g) $2\frac{5}{6}$ h) $5\frac{1}{4}$

i) $6\frac{1}{4}$ j) $4\frac{2}{5}$ k) $7\frac{5}{6}$ l) $5\frac{9}{10}$

Page 22

1. a) $\frac{9}{4}$ b) $\frac{14}{3}$

c) $\frac{27}{5}$ d) $\frac{23}{6}$

2. a) $\frac{19}{5}$ b) $\frac{17}{3}$ c) $\frac{31}{6}$ d) $\frac{34}{5}$

e) $\frac{38}{7}$ f) $\frac{41}{9}$ g) $\frac{67}{10}$ h) $\frac{35}{8}$

Page 23

1. a) $\frac{1}{3}$ b) $\frac{1}{4}$ c) $\frac{1}{5}$ d) $\frac{1}{5}$

e) $\frac{2}{5}$ f) $\frac{2}{7}$ g) $\frac{2}{5}$ h) $\frac{2}{7}$

i) $\frac{4}{5}$ j) $\frac{3}{4}$ k) $\frac{5}{6}$ l) $\frac{1}{8}$

2. $\frac{1}{2}$, $\frac{1}{5}$, $\frac{2}{5}$, $\frac{1}{4}$, $\frac{1}{10}$, $\frac{3}{4}$

3. $\frac{1}{5}$, $\frac{1}{10}$, $\frac{2}{5}$, $\frac{3}{10}$, $\frac{2}{25}$, $\frac{18}{25}$

4. $\frac{1}{10}$, $\frac{1}{20}$, $\frac{3}{10}$, $\frac{3}{4}$, $\frac{11}{20}$, $\frac{3}{25}$

Page 24

1. Two equivalent fractions in each case, e.g.

a) $\frac{6}{10}$ or $\frac{9}{15}$ b) $\frac{10}{16}$ or $\frac{50}{80}$

c) $\frac{2}{3}$ or $\frac{60}{90}$ d) $\frac{5}{7}$ or $\frac{20}{28}$

e) $\frac{4}{5}$ or $\frac{8}{10}$ f) $\frac{3}{10}$ or $\frac{15}{50}$

2. a) $\boxed{\frac{4}{10}}$, $\frac{3}{10}$ b) $\frac{2}{8}$, $\boxed{\frac{3}{8}}$

c) $\frac{10}{16}$, $\boxed{\frac{11}{16}}$ d) $\boxed{\frac{6}{9}}$, $\frac{5}{9}$

e) $\frac{9}{24}$, $\boxed{\frac{11}{24}}$ f) $\boxed{\frac{12}{21}}$, $\frac{11}{21}$

3. a) $\frac{7}{9}$ b) $\frac{13}{16}$ c) $\frac{5}{6}$

Page 25

1. a) $\frac{8}{12}$, $\boxed{\frac{9}{12}}$ b) $\boxed{\frac{16}{40}}$, $\frac{15}{40}$

c) $\frac{14}{24}$, $\boxed{\frac{15}{24}}$

2. a) $\frac{1}{3}$, $\frac{4}{9}$, $\frac{2}{3}$ b) $\frac{1}{4}$, $\frac{5}{8}$, $\frac{3}{4}$

c) $\frac{1}{4}$, $\frac{3}{8}$, $\frac{1}{2}$ d) $\frac{2}{5}$, $\frac{1}{2}$, $\frac{7}{10}$

e) $\frac{1}{2}$, $\frac{5}{8}$, $\frac{2}{3}$ f) $\frac{1}{3}$, $\frac{5}{12}$, $\frac{3}{5}$

Answers to Tests

PROGRESS TEST 1 – Page 11

1. a) $\frac{3}{5}$ b) $\frac{3}{8}$ c) $\frac{2}{7}$ d) $\frac{3}{4}$

2. a) 4   b) 3   c) 4   d) 5

3. a) £4   b) 9   c) 10   d) 30

4. a) 12   b) 20   c) 10

5. $\frac{1}{2}$, $\frac{4}{8}$, $\frac{4}{12}$, $\frac{1}{3}$, $\frac{2}{6}$

   $\frac{1}{2}$ and $\frac{4}{8}$ joined, and $\frac{4}{12}$, $\frac{1}{3}$ and $\frac{2}{6}$ joined.

6. Any two fractions equivalent, e.g.

   a) $\frac{2}{6}$ or $\frac{10}{30}$ b) $\frac{4}{10}$ or $\frac{20}{50}$

Total marks = 22

PROGRESS TEST 2 – Page 17

1. a) $\frac{1}{4}$ b) $\frac{1}{3}$ c) $\frac{1}{2}$ d) $\frac{3}{4}$

2. $1\frac{1}{4}$ joined to number line

   $1\frac{3}{4}$ joined to metre sticks

   $1\frac{3}{5}$ joined to chocolate

3. a) $\frac{5}{8}$ b) $\frac{3}{5}$

   c) $\frac{4}{9}$ d) $\frac{5}{12}$

4. $\frac{3}{4}$, $\frac{5}{8}$, $\frac{1}{2}$, $\frac{3}{8}$, $\frac{1}{8}$

5. a) $\frac{2}{6}$ or $\frac{1}{3}$ b) $\frac{3}{12}$ or $\frac{1}{4}$

Total marks = 14

FINAL TEST – Pages 26 to 28

1. a) **1** shaded   b) **3** shaded

   c) **5** shaded

2. a) 4   b) 6

3. $\frac{3}{4}$, $\frac{6}{8}$, $\frac{9}{12}$ in the 1st bag

   $\frac{2}{3}$, $\frac{4}{6}$, $\frac{8}{12}$, $\frac{6}{9}$ in the 2nd bag

   $\frac{5}{6}$, $\frac{10}{12}$, $\frac{15}{18}$ in the 3rd bag

4. a) about **250ml**   b) about **750ml**

   c) about **800ml**

5. a) $\frac{1}{8}$ b) $\frac{2}{5}$ c) $\frac{7}{10}$ d) $\frac{2}{9}$

6. $\frac{1}{5}$, $\frac{3}{10}$, $\frac{1}{2}$, $\frac{3}{5}$, $\frac{7}{10}$

7. $\frac{5}{6}$, $\frac{3}{4}$, $\frac{7}{12}$, $\frac{1}{2}$, $\frac{1}{3}$

8. a) 9   b) 20   c) 16

9. a) $\frac{1}{5}$ b) $\frac{9}{10}$ c) $\frac{1}{20}$

10.

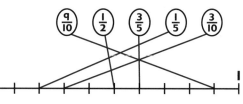

11. a) $2\frac{1}{2}$ b) $2\frac{1}{4}$ c) $2\frac{5}{6}$

12. a) $\frac{23}{6}$ b) $\frac{23}{4}$ c) $\frac{23}{3}$

13. a) $\frac{7}{8}$ b) $\frac{3}{4}$ c) $\frac{9}{14}$

14. a) $\frac{1}{2}$ b) $\frac{3}{4}$ c) $\frac{11}{24}$

15. a) $\frac{12}{18}$, $\left(\frac{15}{18}\right)$, $\frac{14}{18}$

   b) $\frac{18}{24}$, $\left(\frac{21}{24}\right)$, $\frac{18}{24}$

Total marks = 42

Ordering fractions 1

Think of your favourite cake. Would you prefer $\frac{1}{4}$ or $\frac{3}{4}$ of it?

$\frac{3}{4}$ gives you more cake, because the cake is split into 4 pieces and you get 3 of them.

 or

What if the cake was split into eight equal pieces? Would you prefer $\frac{1}{8}$, $\frac{3}{8}$ or $\frac{7}{8}$?

$\frac{7}{8}$ $\frac{3}{8}$ $\frac{1}{8}$ $\frac{7}{8}$ is largest, followed by $\frac{3}{8}$ and $\frac{1}{8}$ is smallest.

1. Write these fractions on the correct posters.

$\frac{1}{8}$ $\frac{5}{6}$ $\frac{3}{4}$ $\frac{7}{10}$ $\frac{4}{9}$ $\frac{3}{7}$ $\frac{2}{5}$ $\frac{5}{8}$

$\frac{3}{5}$ $\frac{5}{9}$ $\frac{4}{5}$ $\frac{4}{7}$ $\frac{2}{3}$ $\frac{3}{8}$ $\frac{4}{10}$ $\frac{1}{3}$

Less than $\frac{1}{2}$	Greater than $\frac{1}{2}$

2. Write these fractions in order, starting with the largest.

a) $\frac{7}{8}$ $\frac{1}{4}$ $\frac{3}{4}$ $\frac{1}{2}$ $\frac{1}{8}$ ___ ___ ___ ___ ___

b) $\frac{1}{6}$ $\frac{2}{3}$ $\frac{5}{6}$ $\frac{1}{3}$ $\frac{1}{2}$ ___ ___ ___ ___ ___

c) $\frac{4}{5}$ $\frac{9}{10}$ $\frac{1}{10}$ $\frac{1}{2}$ $\frac{1}{5}$ ___ ___ ___ ___ ___

Finding fractions of shapes

Remember that fractions are equal parts of things. The shapes below have been split into five equal parts, so each part is one fifth, which we write as $\frac{1}{5}$.

Two fifths, or $\frac{2}{5}$, of these shapes have been shaded.

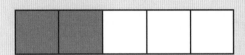
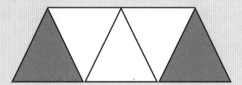

1. Colour the fraction shown.

a) $\frac{3}{5}$

b) $\frac{1}{6}$

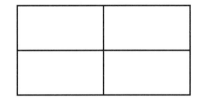

c) $\frac{3}{4}$

d) $\frac{1}{2}$

e) $\frac{3}{4}$

f) $\frac{5}{9}$

g) $\frac{3}{8}$

h) $\frac{1}{3}$

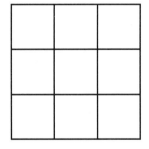
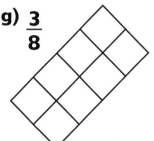
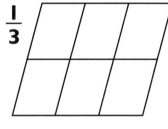

2. What fraction of the larger shape is the smaller shape?

a)

b)

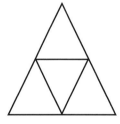

_____

_____

c)

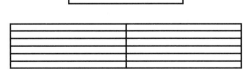

d)

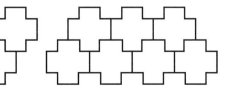

_____

_____

Schofield & Sims | Understanding Maths

1. Paint has been spilt on these pages. About how much of each page has been covered?

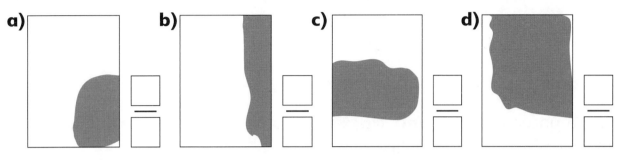

a)   b)   c)   d)

2. Match the mixed numbers to the correct pictures.

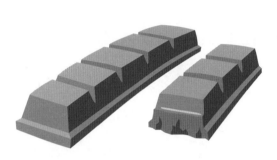

$1\dfrac{1}{4}$

$1\dfrac{3}{4}$

$1\dfrac{3}{5}$

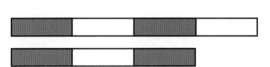

0   1   2

3. Fill in the missing fractions.

a) $\dfrac{3}{8} + \dfrac{\square}{\square} = 1$

b) $\dfrac{2}{5} + \dfrac{\square}{\square} = 1$

c) $\dfrac{\square}{\square} + \dfrac{5}{9} = 1$

d) $\dfrac{\square}{\square} + \dfrac{7}{12} = 1$

4. Write these fractions in order, starting with the **largest**.

$\dfrac{3}{8}$ $\dfrac{3}{4}$ $\dfrac{5}{8}$ $\dfrac{1}{2}$ $\dfrac{1}{8}$ ___ ___ ___ ___ ___

5. What fraction of the larger shape is the smaller shape?

a)

b)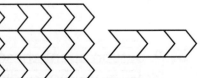

___   ___

Finding fractions of numbers

On page 6 we learned how to find **unit fractions** of numbers, like $\frac{1}{3}$ of **12** and $\frac{1}{6}$ of **18**. Unit fractions always have a numerator of **1**. Look back to page 6 if you're not sure.

To find $\frac{1}{6}$ of 18 we divide 18 by 6 $18 \div 6 = 3$ so $\frac{1}{6}$ **of 18 = 3**

Once you can find a **unit fraction** of a number you can find **any** fraction of a number by multiplying, like this:

$\boxed{\frac{3}{5}}$ of **10** first find $\frac{1}{5}$ of **10** **one** fifth of **10** = **10** ÷ **5** = **2**,

then **multiply** by the number of fifths you have (the numerator)

one fifth of **10** = **2** and so **three** fifths of **10** = **3** × **2** = **6**

Find the unit fraction first, then **multiply** to find other fractions, like this:

$\boxed{\frac{5}{8}}$ of **32** **32 ÷ 8 = 4** **5 × 4 = 20**

One eighth of **32** five-eighths of **32**

1. Find:

a) $\frac{2}{3}$ of **12** _____

b) $\frac{2}{3}$ of **18** _____

c) $\frac{3}{4}$ of **16** _____

d) $\frac{3}{4}$ of **20** _____

2. Find:

a) $\frac{3}{8}$ of **16** _____

b) $\frac{3}{8}$ of **24** _____

c) $\frac{5}{8}$ of **32** _____

d) $\frac{5}{8}$ of **40** _____

e) $\frac{3}{4}$ of **40** _____

f) $\frac{5}{6}$ of **36** _____

g) $\frac{7}{9}$ of **27** _____

h) $\frac{7}{10}$ of **80** _____

3. Find three-quarters of:

a) **24** _____

b) **32** _____

c) **48** _____

d) **60** _____

4. Find four-fifths of:

a) **30** _____

b) **40** _____

c) **25** _____

d) **45** _____

5. A person spent these fractions of one day (24 hours) on different activities. How many hours did they spend on each?

a) $\frac{3}{12}$ _____

b) $\frac{5}{24}$ _____

c) $\frac{3}{8}$ _____

d) $\frac{1}{6}$ _____

Do you remember that **equivalent fractions** have the same value but are made using different digits? Look back to pages 8–10 if you're not sure.

All of the fractions below are **equivalent** to one half.

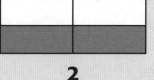

$$\frac{2}{4}$$

$$\frac{3}{6}$$

$$\frac{4}{8}$$

$$\frac{5}{10}$$

To find fractions that are **equivalent** you can **multiply** or **divide** the top *and* bottom numbers by the same number.

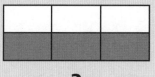

$\div 2$ $\frac{2}{4}$ $\frac{1}{2}$ $\div 2$

$\times 3$ $\frac{1}{2}$ $\frac{3}{6}$ $\times 3$

$\times 4$ $\frac{1}{2}$ $\frac{4}{8}$ $\times 4$

$\div 5$ $\frac{5}{10}$ $\frac{1}{2}$ $\div 5$

These fractions are all **equivalent** to one half.

1. Find **8** sets of equivalent fractions. Write them below.

$\frac{1}{2}$	$\frac{3}{8}$	$\frac{5}{6}$	$\frac{1}{4}$	$\frac{6}{16}$	$\frac{4}{10}$	$\frac{1}{3}$	$\frac{10}{12}$	$\frac{2}{8}$	$\frac{2}{5}$
$\frac{1}{5}$	$\frac{8}{20}$	$\frac{15}{18}$	$\frac{10}{20}$	$\frac{1}{7}$	$\frac{2}{6}$	$\frac{6}{12}$	$\frac{10}{30}$	$\frac{5}{15}$	$\frac{3}{15}$
$\frac{4}{20}$	$\frac{3}{9}$	$\frac{5}{10}$	$\frac{5}{25}$	$\frac{50}{100}$	$\frac{16}{40}$	$\frac{2}{10}$	$\frac{4}{16}$	$\frac{4}{12}$	$\frac{2}{14}$

Set a _____   Set b _____

Set c _____   Set d _____

Set e _____   Set f _____

Set g _____   Set h _____

2. Write two more equivalent fractions in each of the sets of fractions you have made.

Fractions on a number line

Did you know... Fractions and mixed numbers lie between whole numbers.
Here are some that lie between **3** and **4**.

3   **3$\frac{1}{4}$**   **3$\frac{2}{5}$**   **3$\frac{1}{2}$**   **3$\frac{3}{5}$**   **3$\frac{3}{4}$**   **4**

There are an infinite number of them that lie between any two whole numbers.

We can mark fractions on a number line between two whole numbers
by splitting the line into equal parts. The denominator (bottom
number) tells us how many parts to split the line into. We can mark
$\frac{1}{3}$ and $\frac{2}{3}$ on this line by splitting the line into thirds.

0 $\frac{1}{3}$ $\frac{2}{3}$ **1**

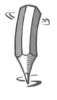

1. Join each fraction to its correct position on the line.

a)

0   **1**

$\frac{3}{5}$ $\frac{2}{5}$ $\frac{4}{5}$ $\frac{1}{5}$

b)

0   **1**

$\frac{3}{8}$ $\frac{1}{2}$ $\frac{5}{8}$ $\frac{7}{8}$ $\frac{1}{8}$

c)

0   **1**

$\frac{3}{10}$ $\frac{2}{5}$ $\frac{4}{5}$ $\frac{7}{10}$ $\frac{1}{10}$ $\frac{9}{10}$

2. Write the fractions the arrows are pointing to. Think about equivalent
fractions!

a)

0   **1**

$\frac{}{1}$ $\frac{}{2}$

b)

0   **1**

 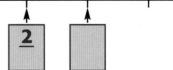

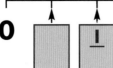

$\frac{}{1}$ $\frac{}{2}$ $\frac{}{2}$ $\frac{}{5}$

Mixed numbers and improper fractions 1

Do you remember that numbers like $3\frac{1}{2}$, $4\frac{1}{4}$ and $6\frac{3}{4}$ are called **mixed numbers** because they are a mixture of whole numbers and fractions?

In this picture, **7** quarters are shaded:

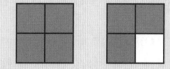

We can write this in two ways:

seven-quarters $\frac{7}{4}$ or   one whole and three quarters $1\frac{3}{4}$

This is called an **improper fraction** as the **numerator** (number on top) is **larger** than the **denominator** (number on bottom).

This is called a **mixed number** because it has a whole number *and* a fraction.

Changing improper fractions to mixed numbers

Change $\frac{13}{4}$ to a mixed number.

'How many lots of the denominator are in the numerator?' *How many **4s** in **13**?*

Find the answer and write it with a remainder........... **3 r 1**

The first number is the whole number.

The remainder tells you the numerator of the fraction.

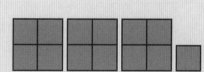

$3\frac{1}{4}$

1. Change these improper fractions to mixed numbers.

a) $\frac{3}{2}$ _____

b) $\frac{7}{2}$ _____

c) $\frac{5}{3}$ _____

d) $\frac{7}{4}$ _____

e) $\frac{17}{10}$ _____

f) $\frac{13}{5}$ _____

g) $\frac{17}{6}$ _____

h) $\frac{21}{4}$ _____

i) $\frac{25}{4}$ _____

j) $\frac{22}{5}$ _____

k) $\frac{47}{6}$ _____

l) $\frac{59}{10}$ _____

Changing mixed numbers to improper fractions

Change $2\frac{3}{4}$ to an improper fraction.

$2\frac{3}{4}$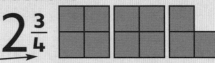

Look at the denominator.
We need to change this fraction into quarters.

How many quarters are in $2\frac{3}{4}$?

There are **8** quarters in the **2** wholes and **3** quarters more.
So there are **11** quarters in $2\frac{3}{4}$.

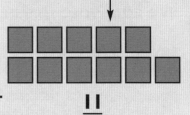

$\frac{11}{4}$

1. Change these mixed numbers to improper fractions.

a) $2\frac{1}{4}$ _____

b) $4\frac{2}{3}$ _____

c) $5\frac{2}{5}$ _____

d) $3\frac{5}{6}$ _____

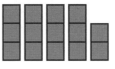

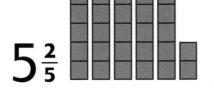

We can use multiplication to do this more quickly:

Change $3\frac{5}{6}$ to an improper fraction.

Step 1: multiply the **whole number** by the **denominator** $3 \times 6 = 18$
(This gives how many sixths there are in the 3 whole ones)

Step 2: add on the numerator (the extra sixths)... $18 + 5 = 23$
(This gives the numerator of the improper fraction)

The denominator stays the same.   So $3\frac{5}{6} = \frac{23}{6}$

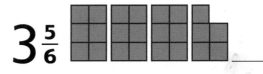

2. Change these mixed numbers to improper fractions.

a) $3\frac{4}{5}$ _____

b) $5\frac{2}{3}$ _____

c) $5\frac{1}{6}$ _____

d) $6\frac{4}{5}$ _____

e) $5\frac{3}{7}$ _____

f) $4\frac{5}{9}$ _____

g) $6\frac{7}{10}$ _____

h) $4\frac{3}{8}$ _____

Simplest form

Changing a fraction to its simplest form is sometimes called **reducing to lowest terms** or **cancelling**. It is about finding an **equivalent fraction** where the numerator and denominator are as small as they can be.

To change a fraction to its simplest form:

Just **divide** the numerator **and** the denominator by the largest number you can. When you can't divide again by any other number the fraction is in its **simplest (or lowest) form**. These fractions have been cancelled to their simplest form:

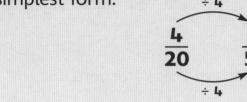 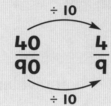 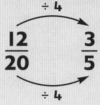

1. Change these fractions to their simplest form.

a) $\dfrac{30}{90}$ _____

b) $\dfrac{10}{40}$ _____

c) $\dfrac{6}{30}$ _____

d) $\dfrac{9}{45}$ _____

e) $\dfrac{20}{50}$ _____

f) $\dfrac{10}{35}$ _____

g) $\dfrac{8}{20}$ _____

h) $\dfrac{6}{21}$ _____

i) $\dfrac{24}{30}$ _____

j) $\dfrac{42}{56}$ _____

k) $\dfrac{45}{54}$ _____

l) $\dfrac{12}{96}$ _____

2. What fraction of **20** is each of these numbers? Give fractions in their simplest form.

3. What fraction of **50** is each of these numbers? Give fractions in their simplest form.

4. What fraction of **100** is each of these numbers? Give fractions in their simplest form.

Common denominators

Equivalent fractions

On page 19 you learned how to change fractions into **equivalent fractions** by **multiplying** or **dividing** the numerator and denominator by the same number.

So $\frac{9}{36}$ is equivalent to $\frac{1}{4}$ because we can **divide** the numerator and denominator by **9**.

And $\frac{2}{5}$ is equivalent to $\frac{10}{25}$ because we can **multiply** each by **5**.

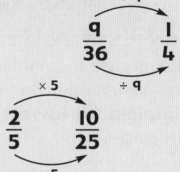

1. Write two fractions that are equivalent to each of these fractions.

a) $\frac{3}{5}$ _____ _____

b) $\frac{5}{8}$ _____ _____

c) $\frac{6}{9}$ _____ _____

d) $\frac{10}{14}$ _____ _____

e) $\frac{20}{25}$ _____ _____

f) $\frac{30}{100}$ _____ _____

Common denominators

Sometimes, if we need to compare or order fractions, we have to find equivalent fractions with 'a common denominator'. This means changing one or more of the fractions so they have the same denominator.

Which is larger $\frac{3}{5}$ *or* $\frac{7}{10}$?

Change $\frac{3}{5}$ into tenths by multiplying the top and bottom by **2**:

Now we have $\frac{6}{10}$ and $\frac{7}{10}$ and it's easier to see that $\frac{7}{10}$ is larger.

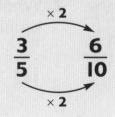

2. Change these fractions so they have a common denominator. Circle the larger fraction in each pair.

a) $\frac{2}{5}$ or $\frac{3}{10}$ _____

b) $\frac{1}{4}$ or $\frac{3}{8}$ _____

c) $\frac{5}{8}$ or $\frac{11}{16}$ _____

d) $\frac{2}{3}$ or $\frac{5}{9}$ _____

e) $\frac{3}{8}$ or $\frac{11}{24}$ _____

f) $\frac{4}{7}$ or $\frac{11}{21}$ _____

3. Circle the largest fraction in each part.

a) $\frac{2}{3}$ $\frac{7}{9}$ $\frac{13}{18}$

b) $\frac{3}{4}$ $\frac{13}{16}$ $\frac{5}{8}$

c) $\frac{7}{12}$ $\frac{5}{6}$ $\frac{19}{24}$

Schofield & Sims | Understanding Maths

Sometimes you have to change the fractions to a new common denominator.

Which is larger $\frac{3}{4}$ or $\frac{5}{6}$?

We can't change quarters into sixths.
So, look at both denominators.

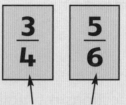

Ask 'What is the lowest number that **both 4** and **6** divide into with no remainders?' The lowest number is **12**. So change both fractions to **equivalent** ones with the denominator **12**.

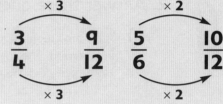

Now we have $\frac{9}{12}$ and $\frac{10}{12}$. $\frac{10}{12}$ is larger, so the answer to the question is $\frac{5}{6}$

1. Change both these fractions so they have a common denominator. Circle the larger fraction in each pair.

a) $\frac{2}{3}$ or $\frac{3}{4}$ _____

b) $\frac{2}{5}$ or $\frac{3}{8}$ _____

c) $\frac{7}{12}$ or $\frac{5}{8}$ _____

Sometimes we need to find a common denominator for **three** fractions.

Put these fractions in order, smallest first: $\frac{5}{6}$, $\frac{7}{8}$ or $\frac{3}{4}$

Ask 'What is the lowest number that **6, 8** and **4** divide into with no remainders?'

The lowest number is **24**. Change each fraction to an equivalent fraction with a denominator of **24**

Now we have $\frac{20}{24}$, $\frac{21}{24}$ and $\frac{18}{24}$. In order of size this is $\frac{18}{24}$, $\frac{20}{24}$ and $\frac{21}{24}$

So the answer to the question is $\frac{3}{4}$, $\frac{5}{6}$ and $\frac{7}{8}$

2. Put these fractions in order, smallest first, using common denominators.

a) $\frac{1}{3}$ $\frac{2}{3}$ $\frac{4}{9}$ _____ _____ _____

b) $\frac{5}{8}$ $\frac{1}{4}$ $\frac{3}{4}$ _____ _____ _____

c) $\frac{3}{8}$ $\frac{1}{4}$ $\frac{1}{2}$ _____ _____ _____

d) $\frac{2}{5}$ $\frac{7}{10}$ $\frac{1}{2}$ _____ _____ _____

e) $\frac{1}{2}$ $\frac{2}{3}$ $\frac{5}{8}$ _____ _____ _____

f) $\frac{1}{3}$ $\frac{3}{5}$ $\frac{5}{12}$ _____ _____ _____

1. Colour the fraction shown.

a) $\frac{1}{5}$

b) $\frac{3}{8}$

c) $\frac{5}{6}$

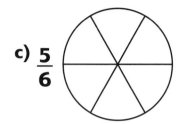

2. Answer these questions mentally.

a) A football team played 24 matches in a season. They won $\frac{1}{6}$ of them. How many did they win?

b) **One fifth** of the sweets in a bag are red. There are 30 sweets in the bag. How many are red?

3. Write any equivalent fractions from the poster in the correct bags.

$\frac{3}{4}$ $\frac{2}{3}$ $\frac{5}{6}$

$\frac{8}{12}$ $\frac{6}{9}$

$\frac{9}{12}$ $\frac{10}{12}$

$\frac{15}{18}$ $\frac{4}{6}$

$\frac{5}{8}$ $\frac{6}{8}$

4. These jugs each hold 1000 millilitres when they are full. About how many millilitres are in the jugs now?

a)

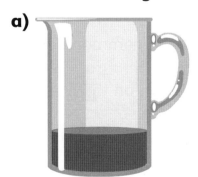

b)

c)

about _____ ml   about _____ ml   about _____ ml

5. Fill in the missing fractions.

a) $1 - \dfrac{7}{8} = \dfrac{\square}{\square}$

b) 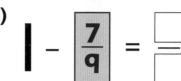 $1 - \dfrac{3}{5} = \dfrac{\square}{\square}$

c) $1 - \dfrac{3}{10} = \dfrac{\square}{\square}$

d) $1 - \dfrac{7}{9} = \dfrac{\square}{\square}$

6. Write these fractions in order, smallest first.

$\dfrac{3}{5}$ $\dfrac{3}{10}$ $\dfrac{1}{5}$ $\dfrac{1}{2}$ $\dfrac{7}{10}$ ____ ____ ____ ____ ____

7. Write these fractions in order, largest first.

$\dfrac{7}{12}$ $\dfrac{3}{4}$ $\dfrac{1}{2}$ $\dfrac{1}{3}$ $\dfrac{5}{6}$ ____ ____ ____ ____ ____

8. Find:

a) $\dfrac{3}{8}$ of **24** _____

b) $\dfrac{4}{5}$ of **25** _____

c) $\dfrac{4}{9}$ of **36** _____

9. In its simplest form, what fraction of 100cm is:

a) 20cm? _____

b) 90cm? _____

c) 5cm? _____

10. Join each of the fractions to its correct position on the line.

$\dfrac{9}{10}$ $\dfrac{1}{2}$ $\dfrac{3}{5}$ $\dfrac{1}{5}$ $\dfrac{3}{10}$

0 |————|————|————|————|————|————|————|————|————|————| **1**

11. Change these improper fractions to mixed numbers.

a) $\dfrac{5}{2}$ _____

b) $\dfrac{9}{4}$ _____

c) $\dfrac{17}{6}$ _____

12. Change these mixed numbers to improper fractions.

a) $3\dfrac{5}{6}$ _____

b) $5\dfrac{3}{4}$ _____

c) $7\dfrac{2}{3}$ _____

13. Change these fractions to their simplest form.

a) $\dfrac{70}{80}$ _____

b) $\dfrac{24}{32}$ _____

c) $\dfrac{45}{70}$ _____

14. Which is larger?

a) $\dfrac{2}{5}$ or $\dfrac{1}{2}$ _____

b) $\dfrac{3}{4}$ or $\dfrac{5}{8}$ _____

c) $\dfrac{5}{12}$ or $\dfrac{11}{24}$ _____

15. Change these fractions so they have a common denominator.
Circle the largest fraction in each set.

a) $\dfrac{2}{3}$ $\dfrac{5}{6}$ $\dfrac{7}{9}$ ____ ____ ____

b) $\dfrac{9}{12}$ $\dfrac{7}{8}$ $\dfrac{3}{4}$ ____ ____ ____